Magic Mates
Go Wild!

J

Illustrated by

Stik

RISING ★ STARS

Rising Stars UK Ltd.
22 Grafton Street, London W1S 4EX
www.risingstars-uk.com

The right of Jane West to be identified as the author of this work
has been asserted by her in accordance with the Copyright, Design
and Patents Act 1988.

Published 2008

Cover design: Button plc
Illustrator: Stik, Bill Greenhead for Illustration
Text design and typesetting: Andy Wilson
Publisher: Gill Budgell
Editor: Jane Wood

British Library Cataloguing in Publication Data.
A CIP record for this book is available from the British Library

ISBN: 985 1 84680 335 2

Printed in the UK by CPI Bookmarque, Croydon, CR0 4TD

Mixed Sources
Product group from well-managed
forests and other controlled sources
www.fsc.org Cert no. TT-COC-002227
© 1996 Forest Stewardship Council

Contents

Meet the Magic Mates

The Magic Mates are best friends –
but that doesn't mean they're all alike.

Name: 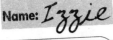 *Izzie*

The sporty one: can climb trees,
surf and take on the boys
at their own game – and win.

Travels by: running!

Loves: trendy tracksuits, open skies
and sandy beaches.

Hates: standing still.

Name: *Meena*

The girly one: uses her mobile
for networking and planning
her social life.

Travels by: Mum's car (her personal
chauffeur).

Loves: pink and her Magic Mates.

Hates: breaking a nail.

4

Name: *Ginger*

The ginger one: you don't wanna mess with this feisty gal – the Kung Fu and quick quip queen!

Travels by: push-scooter.

Loves: Jackie Chan and her Magic Mate pals.

Hates: nail extensions.

Name: Jo

The clever one: uses her brains and quick wit to talk her way out of trouble. Sometimes she's a bit too quick.

Travels by: bicycle and is designing a pair of motorised rollerblades.

Loves: Jacqueline Wilson, Cathy Cassidy and Albert Einstein.

Hates: being called 'geek', 'nerd', 'swot' or 'boffin'.

Name: Ellie

The fashion-conscious one: can tell her Prada from her Asda and knows how to accessorise.

Travels by: limousine, of course! (But only in her dreams.)

Loves: shopping.

Hates: anything to do with getting dirty; anyone who upsets her Magic Mates.

Name: Yash

The funky punky one: the 'alternative' one of the gang who hugs trees, people and furry animals.

Travels by: skateboard.

Loves: having a good time.

Hates: bullies.

1

Getting Into the Swing of Things

It's Ginger's birthday. As a special treat, Ginger and her Magic Mates are going to an adventure park.

They're all looking forward to a fun day
out. But Ginger has forgotten to tell them
exactly what sort of adventure park
they're going to.

Meena   I love fun fairs! I like going
on the Big Wheel and looking
at everyone down below.

Ginger   Er, well …

Ellie   Oh, yes! And eating candyfloss!

Izzie   And the Dodgems …

Ginger It's not really …

Jo   And the Haunted House
            with those funny mirrors.
            They make me laugh.

Yash   And the Waltzers! The louder
you scream, the faster
they spin you!

Ginger   No, listen …

Ellie   I don't like all that boy stuff,
but I do like going on the dance
machines.

Meena   Yes, that sounds like fun.

Ginger   No. Listen to me. You've all
got it wrong. We're not going
to that sort of fun fair.
I said we're going to an
adventure park.

Yash   Isn't it the same thing?

Ginger   No, it's very different.
It's more like … er … climbing
and jumping and swinging
through the trees.

Yash   Wicked!

Jo   It sounds like one of those
training courses they do
in the army.

Izzie   Fantastic!

Going Wild!

The Go Wild! adventure park is in a steep, wooded valley. All the instructors have muddy boots and wear combat trousers.

Yash and Izzie are grinning from ear to ear. Jo looks curious. Ellie looks worried and Meena looks like she's going to cry.

Oh dear! Ginger wants everyone to be happy for her birthday treat.

Ginger It'll be fun. I promise! At least …
at least give it a chance.

Meena Of course we'll give it a chance,
won't we, Ellie?

Ellie Yes. It's your birthday, Ginger,
and we're your Magic Mates.
What's a birthday without us?

Meena   That's right – Magic Mates stick together.

Ellie   Just don't leave us behind, will you?

Ginger   You're the best! And I won't leave you behind, I promise.

The Magic Mates listen to the safety instructions. Their instructor, David, makes them feel very safe.

Even Ellie and Meena start to think that the adventure park might be fun.

David   If you get stuck, I'll be there to help you. But the most important thing is to have fun.

Ginger, Yash, Izzie, Jo
          We will!

Ellie, Meena
          We'll try!

Soon the girls are …

… crawling through
tunnels …

… climbing trees …

… swinging like Tarzan

... walking the plank ...

... going up rope ladders ...

... and crossing
wobbly bridges.

The girls are having great fun. Even Ellie and Meena are enjoying themselves. There's just one challenge left – the Zip Wire. It's very high up. Very high up indeed. It's a long, long way down.

No Pain, No Gain

The Zip Wire is the last challenge. Yash, Izzie, Jo and Meena are already on their way down. Meena has her eyes closed. Ginger and Ellie are waiting for their turn. Ginger is excited but Ellie is scared.

Ginger   Wow! I can't wait to try that!

Ellie   I don't think I can do this,
Ginger. It's too high.
You go. I'll walk back.

Ginger   No way! I promised I wouldn't
leave you. If you don't do it,
I won't either.

Ellie   I don't want to spoil your
birthday! That's not fair.
I'll just walk back. I'll be fine.

Ginger   No. Magic Mates stick together.
I won't let you down.

Some boys hear them talking.

Boy 1   Ah! Poor little cry-baby!

Boy 2   Ha, ha, ha!
She's afraid of the Zip Wire!

Ginger   Just shut up! Ellie's not
a cry-baby. She's really brave.

Boy 1   I think she's a wuss!

Ellie   I'm busy now. I'll have to
ignore you some other time.

Boy 3   She thinks she's funny,
but she's a real scaredy-cat.

Ellie   Are you usually this annoying
        or is today a special day?

Boy 1   Whatever. Race you down –
        if you dare.

Boy 3   No pain, no gain!

The boys zoom down the Zip Wire.
Ellie doesn't know what to do.
She's scared but she doesn't want Ginger
to miss her turn. And she can't let
those rude boys know how scared she is.
What will she do?

Success Comes in Cans, Not Can't's

Ginger and Ellie are still standing at the top of the Zip Wire. It's a long walk back or a long way down. It's up to Ellie to choose. Ginger has an idea.

Ginger   We could ask David to come and help you.

Ellie   No. I'm sorry, Ginger, but I just can't do it. I know I talked big with those boys, but it's so high up. It really scares me.

Ginger Okay. Don't worry about it, Ellie.
Let's walk back and then
we can all have some
of my birthday cake together.

Just then someone else arrives
at the Zip Wire. She looks like
somebody's granny with her white hair –
but where did she get those
combat trousers?

Granny   Hello, girls. Have you seen
my grandson? He's got
a striped top. He's with
two of his friends.

Ginger   Yes, he was here a minute ago.
They went down the Zip Wire.

Granny   Wow! I thought he'd be too
scared to do that. I guess
he didn't want to lose face
in front of his friends. Are you
going down the Zip Wire?

Ginger   No, we're walking back.

Granny   That's a shame. It's the best bit.
It feels like you're flying.

Ginger   Have you done it before?

Granny   Oh, yes! I've been here lots of
times with my grandchildren.
I have eight, you see.
The Zip Wire is my favourite,
although I do like to monkey
around on the Tarzan Swings.

Ginger   I love going on the Tarzan
Swings, too! They are really
good fun.

Granny   Then you must try the Zip Wire.
You'll love it.

Ginger   Er ... no thanks.
We're walking back.

Ellie   It's all my fault. I'm scared
because it's so high up.
I can't do it. Ginger won't let me
walk back by myself.

Granny What a good friend she is.
But remember: 'Success comes
in cans, not can'ts'. That's
something my mum used to say
to me. If you tell yourself
you can't do something,
then you won't be able to do it.
If you tell yourself you can,
the whole world is waiting
for you.

Ellie I wish I was as brave as you.

Granny I'm not brave,
I'm stubborn!
Just because
I'm 72 and have white hair,
people keep telling me
I can't do things. 'Take care',
'You shouldn't', 'You can't',
'At your age', they say to me.
Well, I'm not going to listen.
It's my life and I say I CAN DO
things … and so can you.

31

5

A Wild Streak

Granny Can-Do gets ready to go down the Zip Wire. Ellie makes up her mind. If Granny Can-Do can fly down the Zip Wire, so can she!

Granny Well done, Ellie!
You are very brave
to overcome your fear.

Ellie I don't think I have overcome
my fear. I'm really scared!

Granny Yes, I know. But you're going
to do it anyway, and that's
what makes you so brave.

Ginger   Yes, you're really brave, Ellie.

Ellie   And you're a Magic Mate,
Ginger.

Granny Here I go!
See you at the bottom!
Wheeeee!

Granny Can-Do races down the Zip Wire.
Her white hair flies in the wind and she's
shouting with excitement.

Ellie   Isn't she amazing?

Ginger   Yes! And so are you!
I've fixed the safety ropes.
You'll be fine, Ellie.
I'll be right behind you.
In two minutes we'll be eating
birthday cake.

Ellie   Okay, this is it. Here goes!

Ellie closes her eyes and steps off
the platform.

Ellie Aaaaaaaaaaagh!
Wheeeee! Wow!

Ginger I'm right behind you, Ellie!
Wheeeee!

In two wonderful minutes, the ride is over.
Ellie, Ginger and Granny Can-Do
have all landed safely at the bottom.

Ginger   Wow! That was fantastic!

Ellie   I was scared at first but then it was really good fun.

Granny   I knew you'd enjoy it because you remind me of myself. I was just like you at your age. I had a bit of a wild streak, too.

Ellie　I hope I'm just like you
when I'm 72.

Granny　I'm sure you will be.

Ginger　Thanks for everything.
It's been the best birthday ever!
I've been looking forward
to this ride for ages, and it's twice
as much fun to Go Wild
with all my Magic Mates!

About the Author

Jane West:

- lives by the beach in Cornwall.
- likes bodyboarding.
- loves adventure parks, especially the Tarzan Swings.

Even though she enjoys adventurous stuff like Ginger, she also loves being girly like Ellie! She likes her make-up and nail polish!

Jane has had great fun writing about the Magic Mates and hopes you liked reading about them.

Did You Know?

When babies are born, they are not afraid
of anything. We learn fear as we get older.
Some fears can be useful to help us to stay safe.

I'll stay away from
that flame because it
could burn me.

Some fears are understandable:

That's really
high up. If I fall,
I will get hurt.

Some fears seem to come from nowhere:

I'm scared of spiders, even though I know they can't hurt me.

A phobia is a very strong fear. Phobias are not useful because they stop people from doing things they want to do. With help, many people get over their phobias.

Some fears go away if things are explained. When children learn that thunder can't hurt them, they stop being afraid of the noise.

Sometimes other people can help. If you're afraid of heights, a calm, thoughtful person can help you to feel safe.

All About Tarzan

The Magic Mates enjoy the Tarzan Swings.
This is where you swing on a rope
and jump off at the other side. On some
Tarzan Swings you can get across a river
or a pool of mud. You can land on the grass
or a soft mat. It's great fun!

But do you know why they are called
'Tarzan' Swings?

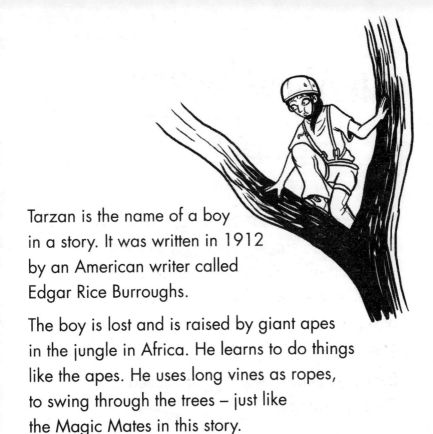

Tarzan is the name of a boy
in a story. It was written in 1912
by an American writer called
Edgar Rice Burroughs.

The boy is lost and is raised by giant apes
in the jungle in Africa. He learns to do things
like the apes. He uses long vines as ropes,
to swing through the trees – just like
the Magic Mates in this story.

Quiz

1 Have you always been afraid of things?

2 What's the point of being scared?

3 What use is a phobia?

4 Where did Tarzan live with the apes?

5 What was Edgar Burroughs'
  tasty middle name?

How did you score?

0–1 Are you monkeying around?

2–3 You're not quite Tarzan, but you're
getting there.

4–5 Go Wild!

Jungle Jokes

Ellie   How do you get a giraffe
in your fridge?

Ginger Open the door, put him in and close
the door.

Ellie   How do you get an elephant
in your fridge?

Ginger Open the door, take the giraffe out,
put the elephant in and close the door.

Ellie   Tarzan, Lord of the Jungle, is having
a meeting with all the animals.
Only one animal isn't there.
Which one is it?

Ginger The elephant, because you left him
in the fridge.

Ellie   Tarzan decides to go and look
for the elephant but he comes to a river
infested with crocodiles. What does
he do?

Ginger Swims across. All the animals have
gone to the meeting!

Magic Mates

RISING ★ STARS